God's Magnum Opus

The Value of a Woman

CHALLENGE FOR WOMEN

STUDY GUIDE

VICTORIA BOYSON

God's Magnum Opus

CHALLENGE FOR WOMEN
STUDY GUIDE

God's Magnum Opus
Copyright © 2015
All Rights Reserved.
Published by Kingdom House Press
ISBN 978-0-9906080-5-9

Victoria Boyson Ministries
www.VictoriaBoyson.com
Victoria@Boyson.org

For His Daughters

CONTENTS

God's Magnum Opus

Who do you believe knows the real truth about your value?
(Circle One)

You ◆ Friends ◆ Family ◆ Spouse ◆ Father God

There is only ONE version of the truth about your worth and that is the Father's truth.

(Answers to study guide questions are in the back of the book)

The Father's Truth

1. In the creation story, paradise was not complete until God created

_____.

*Then the LORD God said, "It is **not good** for the man to be alone; I will make him a helper suitable for him." Genesis 2:18.*

God paused in the middle of the sixth day and said,_____,
then He declared_____ after He created woman.

After God created the woman, "*God saw all that He had made, and behold, it was **very good**." Genesis 1:31.*

The words "helper suitable" in Hebrew are more accurately translated as

_____ _____.

ezer = (powerful) helper ◆ kneged = equal

In Hebrew, the meaning of the words God used to describe woman in Genesis 2:18, "*I will make him a helper suitable for him,*" are very interesting. The word "helper" is ezer and is actually translated more accurately to mean "powerful helper." Almost every other time the word ezer is used in scripture, it is referring to God the Holy Spirit.

So imagine, in God, your potential is limitless.

God would not give a gift to Adam of _____, but of equal quality. God doesn't give cheap gifts!

Then God said, "*Let us make human beings in our image, to be like us. They will reign over the fish in the sea, the birds in the sky, the livestock, all the wild animals on the earth, and the small animals that scurry along the ground.*" Genesis 1:26 NIV.

God created Adam and Eve to reign over the earth _____.

Not Property

2. For thousands of years 50% of the population has owned the other 50% of the population, but this was *never* God's idea—He did not condone it.

"*The woman whom You gave to be with me,*" Genesis 3:12.

Eve was created to be Adam's _____ not his _____

God created the greatest, most creative work of art to give to Adam, because He

2

loved him so much. In you the Father created His _____.

You are His work of art, the _____ of His creation masterpiece).

The fall changed man's _____ of the perfect gift he had been given, but it did not change God's truth of who He made you to be.

"*Your desire will be for your husband, and he will rule over you*" Genesis 3:16.

God put the desire for your husband (to be married) in you, but sin unleashed _____ between men and women.

The loving relationship with mutual appreciation God intended would become one of dominance and abuse. His great gift would not be treated as He had created her to be.

God cried when He saw the woman's future, because He saw that sin would cause the strong to prey on the weak. This was not His plan -- it was not His curse, it was the _____ of their sin.

God's plan for an equal friendship and reign between man and woman would be ravaged by the pride and greed released at the fall, but it was still His _____.

God would never allow Satan to destroy His plan for mankind. In Genesis 3:15, He prophesies of the plan of redemption He would unleash to reestablish mankind's rule over the earth.

In your own words describe the meaning of Genesis 3:15 here:

Equal Partners

3. "*In the same way, you husbands must give honor to your wives. Treat your wife with understanding as you live together. She may be weaker than you are, but she is your equal partner in God's gift of new life*" 1 Peter 3:7 NLT.

In Christ, men and women are _____ and both should be treated with equal dignity and honor.

"*So God created human beings in His own image. In the image of God he created them; male and female he created them*" Genesis 1:27 NLT.

By God's design, both male and female were made in His image. Are men more human than women?

If God designed man and wife to be ONE, what is woman's value in the equation?
(Circle One)

Half   ◆   Third   ◆   Fourth   ◆   No value

Shared Tragedy vs. Greek Myth!

4. The idea that Eve was alone with the serpent when she ate the apple and then took it to Adam and he unknowingly ate of the fruit is from _____, not the Word of God.

What are the four words not added in the retelling of the story of the fall of creation in Genesis 3:6 in many translations of scripture?

"The woman was convinced. She saw that the tree was beautiful and its fruit looked delicious, and she wanted the wisdom it would give her. So she took some of the fruit and ate it. Then she gave some to her husband, _____ , and he ate it, too." Genesis 3:6

The tragedy of the fall is _____ by both Adam and Eve. The word "you" in Hebrew has two meanings—it can mean you as in a single person, or plural. The word used in this case has the plural meaning. So, Satan was talking to more than one person, saying,

"[_____] will not certainly die," the serpent said to the woman. "For God knows that when you eat from it your eyes will be opened, and you will be like God, knowing good and evil,"* Genesis 3:4-5. And when Eve answers the serpent, she says "we" in Genesis 3:2.

Things to ponder

If you worked hard to give someone a special gift that cost you a great deal, would you feel bad if the person you gave it to treated it badly or thought badly of it?

Would you be honored to know the gift you gave does not see its own value?

If woman is the expression of God's love presented to mankind, do you think it honors Him when she is dishonored?

Daily Devotions:

Whose truth are you believing about yourself?

List two incidents where you have believed wrongly about yourself:

1.

2.

Make Father God your mirror. "*Every good and perfect gift is from above, coming down from the Father of the heavenly lights, who does not change like shifting shadows*" James 1:17; Romans 16:25; 2 Corinthians 5:17. You are a good and perfect gift sent from the Father—you are God's magnum opus. Think about how carefully He's designed you (Psalm 139:13-14). Thank Father God for making you so perfectly—thank Him for His commitment to you.

Through these Scriptures describe how you believe God sees you:

The Father's Dream
1 Corinthians 1:11

Who do you believe created you?
(Circle One)

You ◆ Friends ◆ Family ◆ Spouse ~ Satan ~ Father God

You were created for great works!

(Answers to study guide questions are in the back of the book)

God is Your Source

1. Where did you come from? Who is your Creator?

"Nevertheless, in the Lord woman is not independent of man, nor is man independent of woman. For as woman came from man, so also man is born of woman. But everything [including women] comes from God" 1 Corinthians 11:11-12 NIV.

Woman came from_____, but every man since then comes from _____.

God created both male and female to _____each other.

Eve was formed using Adam's rib, yet she was still _____creation.

God chose to keep us _____on each other and that dependency is meant to be beautiful, and exemplify the relationship of the Trinity.

"The head (source) of every man is Christ, the head (source) of woman is man, and the head of Christ is God" 1 Corinthians 11:3 NLT.

In Corinthians 11:3 Paul was referring to _____not Christian teachings.

The Greek word kephale in 1 Corinthians 11:3 is better translated as _____rather than head, because it follows the flow of Paul's teaching to the Corinthians.

Winning the Jews

2. *"To the Jews I became a Jew, to win the Jews"* 1 Corinthians 9:20.

Paul _____like a Jew to win the Jews to Christ and wanted the Corinthian church to do the same.

"You should imitate me, just as I imitate Christ" 1 Corinthians 11:1.

Soul winning was so important to Paul, he asked the church to _____him as he followed Christ.

*"**But among the Lord's people**, women are not independent of men, and men are not independent of women. For although the first woman came from man, every other man was born from a woman, and everything comes from God"* 1 Corinthians 11:11 NLT.

Paul told the Corinthians to imitate him by following the teachings of the Jewish community when they were with the Jews, but _____they were to follow the Christian teachings, which were women and men to live as equal partners.

Was Paul telling the people to live like the Jews only to subjugate women?

Why did Paul want them to follow the teachings of the Jews?

Fighting for Women

3. Why is Satan afraid of you? (Genesis 3:15)

"And I will put enmity between you [Satan] and the woman, and between your offspring (seed) and hers; he (Jesus) will crush your head, and you will strike his heel" Genesis 3:15 NIV (emphasis mine).

The hostility between women and Satan is caused by his _____of you.

Satan realizes the potential of the church, so he has launched a strategy against _____to reduce the effectiveness of at least half of the church.

"God opposes the proud, but gives _____grace to the humble" James 4:6 (emphasis mine).

It is Satan who's launched an attack against men to make them feel superior to _____.

Mankind is without the _____of God when they are blinded by pride. We all need God's grace.

Men are in danger from the blindness pride brings and will continue to be in danger of _____until they recognize women as equals and honor them accordingly.

God's Masterpiece

4. As a woman, you are God's daughter, created as the treasured joy of His own heart. With you, He will bless the world. You are a gift—truly one of the world's

_____.

God loved _____and wanted to give him a gift that would truly express His love toward him; you are that incredible gift. You are the masterpiece of God's love expressed to mankind.

"'At last!' the man exclaimed. 'This one is bone from my bone,and flesh from my flesh! She will be called 'woman,' because she was taken from 'man.'" Genesis 2:23 NLT.

Eve was created from Adam's rib, not to _____her, but so Adam would love her even more.

God wanted Adam to be dependent on Eve and Eve to need Adam. Why?

"No one hates his own body but feeds and cares for it, just as Christ cares for the church" Ephesians 5:29 NLT

If man dishonors woman, he _____because woman was taken from man. If that makes her less than man, then it makes man less also, because to honor women is to honor men.

"I will pour out my Spirit on all people. Your sons and daughters will prophesy, your old men will dream dreams, your young men will see visions. Even on my servants, both men and women, I will pour out my Spirit in those days" Joel 2:28-29 NIV

Satan fears gender _____because he knows unity will draw the blessings of heaven.

Things to ponder:

If God made you, how wonderful are you?

Does being formed from a rib instead of dust make you less valuable than a man?

If Satan is afraid of women, isn't that proof of a woman's value and power?

Daily Devotions:

Who's creation are you? Who designed you?

List two qualities God created in women:

1.

2.

You are who God says you are—read, speak and meditate on what the word says about you. "*May the words of my mouth and the meditation of my heart be pleasing to you, O LORD, my rock and my redeemer*" Psalm 19:14; Psalm 18:2; Psalm 119:18. What you say about yourself has more power to affect you than what others say about you. Write down five giftings God gave you. Think about how much the Lord appreciates you and how proud He is to see you using your gifts.

Through these Scriptures, describe how you believe God designed you to be:

The Concubine's Legacy
Judges 19-20

Who do you believe can turn the grievances of your past into your legacy?
(circle one)

You ◆ Friends ◆ Family ◆ Spouse ◆ Father God

God saw into HISTORY and wanted to show all His girls their true worth!

(Answers to study guide questions are in the back)

Trouble In Israel

1. God wants to show you your value!

In Judges 19, a Levite man from Ephraim was traveling with his concubine. When they arrived at the town of Gibeah, they stayed the night in the home of an older gentleman who lived there.

At his home, a gang of _____gathered around the old man's house and started banging on the door. They demanded the old man give over the Levite man to them so they could have sex with him. (Judges 19:20)

The old man objected vehemently and offered his virgin daughter and the Levite's concubine as a way of escape for the Levite. Yet, before they could refuse his offer, the _____grabbed his _____and shoved her out the door at the gang of men.

The men raped her all night, then let her go. She found her way back to the old man's house, but collapsed on the threshold. In the morning, when the Levite opened the door to leave, he discovered her laying on the doorstep. Giving her a nudge with his foot, he told her to "'_____,' but she had died" Judges 19:28.

He took her body home with him and cut it up into _____ and sent a piece of her to each tribe of Israel. The tribes of Israel were outraged by the shameful act that occurred in their nation and formed an army of _____. Israel gathered at Gibeah and commanded the town to relinquish the men who'd committed the act, but they refused.

The Battle For the Value of a Woman!

2. Instead of surrendering the men, they sent for an army from their tribe (the tribe of Benjamites), and gathered _____to fight against the other tribes of Israel. The Israelites immediately sent troops in to fight against the tribe of Benjamin, but they lost_____.

The next day, Israel went to battle again, but lost _____.
They cried to the Lord and asked Him if they should fight this battle and He said, "_____" (Judges 20:28).

That day, the Israelites ambushed the Benjamite army and drew them out of the city and God did give them the victory. Indeed, it was the tribe of Benjamin this time who lost over _____and the troublemakers were brought to justice.

After three days of battle, over _____lost their lives, all for ONE NAMELESS CONCUBINE!

The Battle for the Value of ONE Woman!

3. The men who were lost were valiant, _____; they were the good guys who wanted to see justice done. Yet, so many men died to fight the battle of this one lone women who wasn't even named in Scripture (Judges 20:17)

You see, to God she was not nameless, He knew her quite well. She was _____to Him. She was a _____ seeking to be loved in a world overwhelmed by the hatred and deception of the fall.

She was His _____and He loved her. His heart needed restitution for the degradation she had suffered. He gave Israel the victory, but He didn't make it easy for them.

God will restore _____after even the most violent devastation against you, because He longs to see you treated as you should be treated. He can make you brand new, because _____are a daughter of the King!

Think about how amazing God really is, then think about how much He loves you. Your amazing heavenly Father _____to redeem your life and make you brand new!

Study the words of John 3:16 and make them personal to you, from your Father to a well-beloved daughter. Write a love letter to yourself from your heavenly Father:

Neglected Truths

4. Through the centuries women have not been treated well. They've been abused, neglected and treated with disdain, but that was _____the way God wanted it to be.

Bathsheba was a Jewish woman who has been maligned through history by those seeking to exonerate King David for the atrocities he committed against her and her husband. She was treated badly, yet _____made it up to her. (We can still love David and yet, recognize that what he did to Bathsheba was very wrong).

Contrary to popular belief, _____did not go willingly to the palace to have an affair with King David. She did not seduce David by bathing naked on her roof. Bathing in the way she did was an accepted custom. David was not supposed to be watching her, but he did.

She was taken by David's men even after he found out she was married, and he lay with her and she got pregnant by him. David had her husband, Uriah, killed so he could marry her and cover his crime. He did not intend to marry her except to cover up what he had done, which proves this was not _____.

She thought no one knew or cared that she had suffered, but _____ did! He saw it all and His heart was enraged. He sent the prophet, Nathan, to confront David and tell him of the consequences of his sin against her God.

God made it up to _____by placing her son on the throne above all of David's other sons.

Do you believe God would defend you and bless you for the hardships you have suffered? He will!

Things to ponder:

Do you believe your heavenly Father wants to restore you? Do you believe He can?

Do you believe God will make your innocence shine like the dawn as stated in Isaiah?

If the Father violently defended the dignity of the concubine in Judges 19 and 20, can you trust Him to defend you?

Daily Devotions:

Have you allowed the trauma that's attacked you to define you?

List two incidents where the enemy has devalued you and imagine how much God hates what happened to you:

1.

2.

Claim the Word of God for yourself . You are the righteousness of God in Christ. "*I will pour out my Spirit upon all people. Your sons and daughters will prophesy. Your old men will dream dreams, and your young men will see visions. In those days I will pour out my Spirit even on servants—men and women alike.*" Joel 2:28-29; Acts 2:17; Romans 8:1. You've been given a great gift—to be born on the earth at this time is a wonderful thing. Embrace this gift and live for Him. Whatever you do today, do it for Him.

Through these Scriptures, describe how you believe God sees you:

LESSON FOUR

Key To Revival

Who do you think understands the truth of Galatians 3:28 best?
(Circle One)

You ◆ Friends ◆ Family ◆ Spouse ◆ Father God

The cross is God's defense of your value, can you receive it?

(Answers to study guide questions are in the back)

The Cross Realigns Us

1. "*There is neither Jew nor Gentile, neither slave nor free, nor is there male and female, for you are all one in Christ Jesus*" Galatians 3:28. UNITY!!

When you embrace _____, you are no longer a female, but you are one in Christ with His kingdom.

When God looks at you He sees _____!

The cross established heaven's kingdom on earth giving us the _____mankind lost at the fall of creation.

When heaven invades earth, the fallen ideology that separates men and women _____and the chaos and strife that manifested through fall fades as we embrace the kingdom.

Paul said in Galatians 3:28, there is no more bias or prejudice amongst the Lord's people, because we are _____.

If you accept Christ's _____and His salvation, then you must accept the work of His Father's kingdom and His will being made manifest on the earth.

There is now _____male nor female, but just the equality of God's kingdom.

When Heaven Invades Earth

2. Do you believe there is gender bias in heaven?

"*Our Father in heaven, hallowed be your name, your kingdom come, your will be done, _____*" Matthew 6:9-10 NIV.

In God's kingdom there is NO gender bias, we are all _____ loved by the Father!

The Lord taught us to pray for the Father's will to be done on earth. If there's gender equality in heaven, then shouldn't we, as the church, work to encourage gender equality here on earth?

By loving people without _____we reveal Christ's kingdom to the earth!

Women in Revival

3. "*In those days I will pour out my Spirit even on servants—men and women alike!*" Joel 2:28.

When the Holy Spirit manifests Himself on the earth, He eradicates all

_____.

In his book, *Why Not Women*, Loren Cunningham said, "When God begins a dramatic work of His Spirit, women are often in the forefront!"[1]

When God shows up, He erases gender and race barriers, and aligns us with His kingdom. If women are on the forefront when God pours out His Spirit, why would we want to change it back to the post-fall conditions?

After the Azuza Street Revival, William J. Seymour said, "The breaking down of the race and gender barriers was a more sure sign of revival than that of speaking in tongues."

If you agree with his statement, how will it change your life?

We all look forward to revival, but we can have revival as we manifest the way of the kingdom on earth. Let His will be done in you every day as you seek to _____those subjugated by society.

If you want revival, remember _____.

If you want God to use you, just manifest His will on earth

_____.

The Greater Works

4. God has placed you on the earth at this time, because He has planned for your life to be an expression of His love and power. Your life has greater meaning when you live it for Him.

"I tell you the truth, anyone who believes in me will do the same works I have done, and even greater works, because I am going to be with the Father" John 14:12 NLT

You are called to do the _____ of the

_____.

In my book, *God's Magnum Opus,* I share a vision about a building that was only built half way. Think about the part you are called to share in building this building. Are you prepared to serve Him?

We are called to greater works. To do His works, we must get to

_____.

"Go into all the world and preach the gospel to all creation" Mark 16:15 NIV.

There is a whole world out there that has no access to the Word of God; you may be the only Bible some will ever see. What three things can you do to prepare yourself to be used by God?

1_____—Study to show thyself approved (2 Timothy 2:15).

2. _____—Some may never listen to what you say, but they will listen to how you act.

3. _____—Find ways to infiltrate the earth with the knowledge of the love of the Father. (ie. start a youtube channel, start blogging or vlogging—think outside the box of the things you enjoy)

Things to ponder:

How can you bring the manifestation of God's will to the earth?

What can you change in your own thought patterns to manifest heaven on the earth?

If, when the Holy Spirit shows up, all gender and race barriers vanish, wouldn't it make sense to keep it that way?

Daily Devotions:

Are there any areas in your thinking where you may still harbor doubt about who you were created to be?

List two incidents where you've unwittingly accepted gender bias towards yourself, your role as a woman or your capabilities:

1.

2.

Remember Jesus. Through the work of the Cross, we are united into one new man - Jesus. *"There is neither Jew nor Gentile, neither slave nor free, nor is there male and female, for you are all one in Christ Jesus."* Galatians 3:28; Ephesians 2:15; 1 Timothy 1:12. In Christ, we can be freed from insecurity and pride—we are free to love one another. Call someone or write a note to a friend and let them know the gift they are to you.

Through these Scriptures, describe how you believe God sees you:

(1) Why Not Women, Loren Cunningham and David J. Hamilton 2

LESSON FIVE

As It Is In Heaven

Who came to set you free?
(Circle One)

Jesus ◆ Friends ◆ Family ◆ Spouse ◆ Father God

Your Heavenly Father wants to see you freed from the bondage of your past.

(Answers to study guide questions are in the back of the book)

Freedom for the Captives

1. We often quote from Isaiah 61:1, but do we often think about the people this Scripture pertains to? Who are these people who need freedom?

"He has sent me to comfort the brokenhearted and to proclaim that captives will be released and prisoners will be freed" Isaiah 61:1 NLT.

1. Who are the brokenhearted the Lord wants to Comfort?

2. Who are those held in captivity?

3. Who are those who are imprisoned?

Christ came to release captives and set prisoners free. He came to minister to the brokenhearted. Have you ever had a broken heart? Then Christ came to bring _____comfort!

I did a study of missing women and found that in a six month period over 330,000 women went missing and it received no media attention. Christ came to _____those women held captive!

Jesus came to free _____ who've been imprisoned by wrong perceptions held for centuries.

For hundreds of years, black men and women were held in slavery and the scars on the black community remain. They battle something inside themselves; they are _____ by the lies that once held them in captivity. _____ must come to their hearts and minds before it can manifest in their community.

For thousands of years, women were held in _____ and it is barely even recognized as such, yet we harbor a _____ mindset that must be changed by God's Word.

Jesus came to set women free!

Women Ministers

2. You too were called to GO into all the world and PREACH the Gospel!

Many people think Christ had only twelve disciples, because, in the time of Christ, women were not counted. Can you name the other seven women disciples who followed Christ?

"For I did not speak on my own, but the Father who sent me commanded me to say all that I have spoken" John 12:49 NIV. Christ only did the Father's will.

It was the Father's will that Christ establish a new way of thinking about women. He was showing the world what _____ thought of women.

Jesus the Samaritan woman who had been divorced five times into ministry and she brought a _____ of souls to Him!

Jesus Restored Value to Women

3. In John 8, Jesus was confronted by a group of religious leaders who caught a woman in the act of adultery and they wanted Him to render a judgment against her for her crime. The penalty for adultery was death.

The Pharisee's perception of God's gift (women) had been so terribly altered that they esteemed her as little as the cattle they owned. When that property was violated, they wanted _____.

They wondered what Christ would say of the women caught in adultery. They didn't bring the man because he did not fit in to the agenda they had set against Christ. Jesus had defended women in the past, they wondered if He would stick up for this fallen woman.

"What do you say?" the Pharisees demanded of Him in John 8:5 NIV. Jesus _____ on the ground and wrote in the _____.

"When they kept on questioning him, he straightened up and said to them. 'Let any one of you who is without sin be the first to thrown a stone at her'" John 8:7 NIV.

In redirecting the focus on to themselves, Jesus validated the woman's
_____as being equal to theirs.

"The Sabbath was made for man, not man for the Sabbath" Mark 2:27 NIV.

The religious leaders thought they wanted justice until Jesus showed them that His justice would be equal for all. The law was made _____ not man for the law.

_____ matter more than the law!

Affirming Truth
4. In Matthew 19:4-9, the religious leaders challenged Jesus with the law of Moses.

"Is it lawful for a man to _____ his wife for any and every reason?"

"'Haven't you read,' He replied, 'that at the beginning the Creator made them _____ and _____,' and said, 'For this reason a man will leave his father and mother and be _____ to his wife, and the two will become _____.' So they are no longer two, but one flesh. Therefore what _____ has joined together, let no one separate.'"

"'Why then,' they asked, 'did Moses command that a man give his wife a certificate of divorce and _____?'"

"Jesus replied, 'Moses permitted you to divorce your wives because your

_____. *But it was not this way from the beginning. I tell you this, anyone who divorces his wife, except for sexual immorality, and marries another woman* _____" Matthew 19:4-9

It was their blindness that deceived them and Christ knew that, so He reminded them of the Father's _____. By turning their focus back to the Father's design for marriage, He revealed their coldness.

When we fall away from the Father's path for us, we must refocus and reestablish _____ in our lives. The same concepts should be applied to how we value _____.

Things to ponder:

Why did God want men to leave their parents and cling only to their wives?

If men and women are equal, why aren't their more women pastors?

Is the calling on our lives made less by the trauma life throws at us? Does your true value change when you are dishonored by others?

Daily Devotions:

Do you believe God has called you to do great works?

List two incidents in which you have not followed the calling of God for your life because of society's perceptions:

1.

2.

Develop a new picture of yourself . You can recreate your self-image and align your thoughts with His image of you. "*How precious are your thoughts about me, O God. They cannot be numbered! I can't even count them; they outnumber the grains of sand! And when I wake up, you are still with me!*" Psalm 139:17-18; Psalm 33:11; Psalm 36:7. Meditate on the Father's love for you and how much He values you. You are a treasure to everyone lucky enough to meet you.

Through these Scriptures, describe how you believe God sees you:

LESSON SIX

Revolution

Who do you believe understands the calling on your life?
(Circle One)

You ◆ Friends ◆ Family ◆ Spouse ◆ Father God

You were included in Christ's command to preach the Gospel to all the nations!

(Answers to study guide questions are in the back of the book)

The Marginalization of God's Gift

1. Our Creator designed women in His image, He loves us and wants to see us honored and empowered. He is pouring out His power on us and using us for greater works. So, where did misogynistic thinking originate?

Of course destructive objectification against women has always been with us since the fall, but it was the_____ society that really took it to new lows.

Through their plays, poetry and music, they lowered the esteem of women. Because they wanted to use women in perverse ways, they spread the lie that women did not have _____.

The Greek thinking was then adopted by the _____ society, until at last it was adopted by _____ rabbis, who added the teachings to their writings.

One example of the misogynistic beliefs of Jewish men was the prayer they prayed each day: A man must say three blessings every day during morning prayers: He thanks God "that He didn't make me a gentile, that He didn't make me a _____, that He didn't make me an ignoramus."

Bondage Breaker

2. Unraveling misunderstanding of Scripture means looking much deeper at the original meaning of the text, analyzing content and separating truth from fiction.

"*Women should be silent during the church meetings. It is not proper for them to speak. They should be submissive just as the law says. If they have any questions, they should ask their husbands at home, for it is improper for women to speak in church meetings*" 1 Corinthians 14:34-35. (I will address this Scripture at greater length in the next few lessons).

For years this Scripture has been used to keep women from fulfilling the calling on their lives, but was Paul really trying to keep women from ministering?

The letter to the Corinthians was written to bring order to disorder, not of women speaking but of ministry in the church in general. Paul spoke about three ministry gifings: _____

_____ were all new to the Corinthians and did at times bring chaos into the church meetings.

Paul previously stated that he wanted his brothers and sisters in the Lord to _____, so he wasn't now telling them to stop.

Jewish teachings gave women no control over their own body. Their body was considered the property of their husband. Yet, Paul taught that woman had authority over her husband's body and he had authority over hers. This was revolutionary because it meant women had equal rights in marriage. Paul was revolutionizing their view on marriage and giving wives equal value (1 Corinthians 7:14).

Revolutionary or Misogynist

3. Was Paul just another sexist male or was he, in fact, a ground-breaking revolutionary for women?

Paul seems proud to admit that it was a woman who discipled him in the ways of the Lord. It was _____, wife of Aquila, who he said influenced him and strengthened him in the Lord.

Paul referred to Priscilla and her husband as his _____ making them equal to himself. (Romans 16:3)

More than any other apostle, Paul has promoted _____.

He taught men to honor women as ministers of the Gospel and co-laborers.

"*I commend to you our sister Pheobe, a deacon of the church in Cenchreae. I ask you to receive her in the Lord in a way worthy of his people and to give her any help she may need from you, for she has been the benefactor of many people, including me*" _____ (NIV).

When Paul described the qualifications for elders and deacons, he considered them to be the _____ (1 Timothy 3:8-12).

"Greet Andronicus and Junia, my fellow Jews who have been in prison with me. They are outstanding among the apostles, and they were in Christ before I was" Romans 16:7 (NIV).

Paul recognized Junia as an apostle and called her _____ (Romans 16:7)

Paul also recognized the leadership of two women pastors, _____ and _____ who lead churches he supported (Acts 16:40; 1 Corinthians 1:11).

Paul Confronted Ignorance

4. Paul confronted the age-old teaching that forbid men from teaching their wives and daughters anything about the Torah (the old testament scriptures).

Until the time of Christ, women had been subjected to harsh legalistic laws against them and one of those laws was the Scriptures were forbidden them. _____ addressed the fallacy of this law.

"If they have any questions, they should ask their husbands at home, for it is improper for women to speak in church meetings" 1 Corinthians 14:35 NLT.

Most people view this Scripture as one of Paul's "anti-woman" teachings. But with further study we find he wasn't condemning women. He was actually commanding the _____ teach their wives, which they had been previously forbidden to do.

They came to church meetings with no prior knowledge of God and the Scriptures and had a lot of questions. Paul was commanding the men to

_____ them at home so they would have a greater understanding when they met together.

The law which limited women's knowledge of God was an ignorant law. It was that law Paul confronted, not women ministers.

Paul repeatedly taught women how to _____, so obviously he did mean for them to speak in church and minister!

Women Slavery

5. We have to realize that, even though women of the present age have never had to endure what women of the past have endured, we may still feel the effects of it through the gender bias that still permeates our society. It takes generations for the damage of prejudice to be changed, even in our own minds. It takes effort to change our way of thinking about ourselves.

For hundreds of years, Africans and other nationalities have had to endure the effects of _____ and still bare the shame of it to this day. Their lives are affected by the shame brought against the fore-bearers.

The _____ bears the weight of the atrocities they endured during the holocaust.

The _____ came out of 400 years of slavery and still lived under the condemnation of it even though they had been made free. (Numbers 14:14)

Women have been held in slavery, for _____ and no one really recognizes the atrocities they've lived through. Fifty-percent of the world's population was _____ as property with no rights by the other fifty-percent. That is bound to leave scars that need to be removed, even in you and I.

We, as the body of Christ, first need to recognize that women do have
_____ that hinder us. The church, instead of fighting
against women's rights as free individuals, must fight to be a catalyst for their
freedom.

We were told to enjoy our prison, because they believed it pleased God to strip us of
our humanity and chain us to inequality. But that is simply _____
true and it is an affront to His character and His love for His daughters.

Then we should allow our heavenly Father to restore us—He is fully capable!

Pray this over yourself:

"*The Lord is my shepherd, I lack nothing. He makes me lie down in green pastures,
he leads me beside quiet waters, he refreshes my soul. He guides me along the right
paths for his name's sake.*

"*Even though I walk through the darkest valley, I will fear no evil, for you are with
me; your rod and your staff, they comfort me.*

"*You prepare a table before me in the presence of my enemies. You anoint my head
with oil; my cup overflows. Surely your goodness and love will follow me all the days
of my life, and I will dwell in the house of the Lord forever,*" Psalm 23 NIV.

Things to ponder:

If we need healing from the prejudice ideology imposed on women, should we see the
importance of pressing in for our healing and deliverance from this wrong thinking
about ourselves?

Was Paul really sexist or have his teachings been misinterpreted?

Do you believe the mandate of the great commission (Mark 16:15) includes you?

Daily Devotions

What errors from past teachings against women ministers do you feel you need to confront in your own thinking?

List two incidents where you have believed wrongly about women in ministry:

1.

2.

Consider the Kingdom you belong to. You are called to fulfill Christ's prophecy about the church! *"For we were all baptized by one Spirit so as to form one body—whether Jews or Gentiles, slave or free—and we were all given the one Spirit to drink."* 1 Corinthians 12:13. Ezekiel 36:27; Zechariah 12:10. God has a great work for you on this earth, no matter who you are or your age—your life is a seed sown into the kingdom for the glory of your heavenly Father who loves you with all His heart! Meditate about being a part of God's amazing kingdom.

Through these Scriptures, describe how you believe God sees you:

The Way of Love

Who do you believe knows how to truly LOVE you?
(Circle One)

You ◆ Friends ◆ Family ◆ Spouse ◆ Father God

The Father loves you with an everlasting, unchanging, ceaseless love!

(Answers to study guide questions are in the back of the book)

Royal Law

1. The Royal Law of Love rules above ALL other law!

"Yes, indeed, it is good when you obey the royal law as found in the Scripture: 'Love your neighbor as yourself'" James 2:8; Leviticus 19:18.

What many Christians today seem to have passed over as being less important was quite honestly what rocked the world of the early Christians. To them the _____ was revolutionary, since they had come out of an age when religion was used as a tool to dominate people.

Although _____ was an old law, it was made brand new again by Christ!

"Dear friends, I am not writing a new commandment for you; rather it is an old one you have had from the very beginning. This old commandment—to love one another—is the same message you heard before. Yet it is also new. Jesus lived the truth of this commandment, and you also are living it. For the darkness is

disappearing, and the true light is already shining" 1 John 2:7-8 NLT.

The cross brought about the revival of the old royal law of love found in

_____.

This law was the most important law to the _____and they talked about it frequently throughout the new testament. When a law is referenced in the new testament, most likely it is the royal law of love they were referring to.

The way of love exhibited an old law made _____again. It was renewed with examples of how we were to love one another.

The Way of Love

2. The way of love was the way of Christ!

"So now I am giving you a new commandment: Love each other. Just as I have loved you, you should love each other. Your love for one another will prove to the world that you are my disciples" John 13:34-35 NLT.

The way we treat people, all people, including women, identifies us as _____of Christ.

When someone teaches _____that does not line up with the way of love Christ set for us, it shows they do not really know Him.

Never follow a teaching that does not first line up with real love; real love is the love of Christ. The example He gave was _____. (John 13:12-17)

"After washing their feet, he put on his robe again and sat down and asked, 'Do you understand what I was doing? You call me 'Teacher' and 'Lord,' and you are right, because that's what I am. And since I, your Lord and Teacher, have washed your feet, you ought to wash each other's feet. I have given you an example to follow. Do as I have done to you. I tell you the truth, slaves are not greater than their master. Nor is the messenger more important than the one who sends the message. Now that you know these things, God will bless you for doing them'" John 13:12-17 NLT.

The way of love will lead us to _____respect to both genders, all races and people from all social positions.

Jockeying for position or control is _____the way of love, but it is earthly and comes from the remnants of the fall.

If you truly love someone, you would never want them to experience the unhappiness of a forbidden calling. If a husband, father or pastor really love his wife, daughter or female congregant, he would not want to hinder the calling on her life. He would encourage her!

How would you like to be encouraged?

Not So With YOU!

3. Christ taught that we should live our lives contrary to the way of mankind after the fall.

"Jesus called them together and said, 'You know that those who are regarded as rulers of the Gentiles lord it over them, and their high officials exercise authority over them. Not so with you. Instead, whoever wants to become great among you must be your servant, and whoever wants to be first must be slave of all. For even the Son of Man did not come to be served, but to serve, and to give his life as a ransom for many'" Mark 10:42-45 NIV.

In the natural, earthly, fallen nature of man, there is a _____
that is recognized, being master over slave, parent over child and men over women.

In the law of love, however, the Lord commanded that would not be the way with
His followers. Truly, we would be known by _____. We
would treat each other differently and the world would recognize the difference in the
way we treat each other.

We are all ONE and made _____ in Christ (Galatians
3:28)! In the kingdom, the fallen hierarchy should not exist.

*"If anyone claims, 'I am living in the light,' but hates a Christian brother or sister, that
person is still living in darkness"* 1 John 2:9 NLT

If anyone claims to know _____ but chooses to reinforce
the old fallen hierarchy way of living, they do not really know Him.

If someone knows the Lord, they will _____demonize,
demoralize, or degrade women. They will _____treat them
disrespectfully. They WILL treat them as equals and build them up,
_____tear them down.

Living in the light of Christ should be evident by the way we treat
_____, _____and children. Yes,
even children deserve respect! (Ephesians 5:22 - 6:1-9)

This lifestyle should be exemplified in life, not just in
_____.

Spirit-Guided Relationships

4. Relationships are the key to displaying the way of Christ to the lost!

"Be very careful, then, how you live—not as unwise but as wise, making the most of every opportunity, because the days are evil" Ephesians 5:15-16 NIV.

We should be _____how we live and treat others. When we endeavor to treat all people with respect , we display the love of Christ.

If we are prejudice against those we deem less or if we favor those we feel are superior (James 2:1-4 NLT), we are not walking in the

_____.

If we dominate, control or belittle people, if we use people, we are not walking in the _____. Do not follow anyone who treats people this way!

In his letter to the Ephesians, Paul endeavored to reinforce the way of love by focusing on how we treat each other. _____were now equal to their masters: "*And masters, treat your slaves in the same way. Do not threaten them, since you know that he who is both their Master and yours is in heaven, and there is no favoritism with him*" Ephesian 6:9 NIV.

He told the slaves to love their masters and work for them as though they were working for _____ (Ephesians 6:5). Paul was not condoning slavery, but he was working to change the thinking in their hearts. Many work for a "master" of sorts today, when we work for a boss. Paul wanted our work to _____Christ.

He told _____to obey their parents, but he also told parents to treat their children well (Ephesians 6:4). This teaching was also revolutionary.

He told _____to love their lives as they love themselves (Ephesians 5:28), because he knew they would not hate themselves. This was the way of love.

Furthermore, Paul told men to LOVE their wives as much as _____loved the church and He did not demean or belittle the church, but He loved her so much He died for her. The commands Paul gave the church refocused all our relationships back to _____.

He told the wives to submit to their husbands, but he said this right after he told all of us to *"Submit to one another out of reverence for Christ"* Ephesians 5:21 NLT.

Defining Submission

5. The church should never mention submission unless they first take the time to define what it is and what it is not!

Submission is not the same as obedience. _____ is the voluntary yielding of one's self and ideas to another person.

It cannot be demanded or forced, because it is not the same as _____—voluntary indicates you have a choice.

Only slaves and children were told to obey, which is not voluntary. Obedience gives us no rights, whether male or female, but submission is a _____.

We all have the right to either submit or not, as guided by wisdom and conscience. If we are not using our wisdom and conscience to determine on a case by case basis whether to submit, then it is not _____, but it has become obedience.

Based on your reason and conscience, submitting FIRST to God, you will either agree with someone's idea or council or you will disagree. If you agree, then you have _____ to their wisdom, because you feel it is better as led by wisdom and conscience. Quite obviously, in any relationship we submit to one another constantly through life, but we do not do so because it is

_____.

Submission to any human never trumps your submission to God. He always comes first!

If we demand submission, then we strip the other person of their reason and conscience and have then robbed them of their _____. God gave both men and women brains and He wants us to use them.

If we do not define what _____is, we leave every person to define it by their life's experiences and sometimes those experiences are abusive and we inadvertently condone abuse.

_____for all people, is a big deal to God and our religion is not His if we use it to strip others of the humanity He has given them.

Things to ponder:

What is the royal law of love or the way of love?

What is the old and new commandment Christ gave us and why should we let it become law in our hearts?

Does it reveal the love of the Father to a woman to strip her of her calling simply because she is a woman?

Is it more important to submit to God or other people?

Daily Devotions

In what ways have you seen that you've been guided by others who've not walked in love toward you?

List two incidents where you have believed you were a second-class human because of incorrect theology:

1.

2.

Let yourself believe what God has said about you. Like yourself, enjoy yourself. *"For you created my inmost being; you knit me together in my mother's womb. I praise you because I am fearfully and wonderfully made; your works are wonderful, I know that full well"* Psalm 139:13-14; Psalm 139:73; Isaiah 44:24. Think about the fact that you were created to give God joy! He delights in you. Today, make Him your delight!

Through these Scriptures, describe how you believe God sees you:

Honoring God's Word

Who do you think could better empower you to fulfill your calling?
(Circle One)

You ◆ Friends ◆ Family ◆ Spouse ◆ Father God

The Father knows your calling better than you do and He will love you into the plan He has for you.

(Answers to study guide questions are in the back of the book)

What is Love?

1. Love does NOT dishonor!

"Love is patient, love is kind. It does not envy, it does not boast, it is not proud. It does not dishonor others, it is not self-seeking, it is not easily angered, it keeps no record of wrongs. Love does not delight in evil but rejoices with the truth. It always protects, always trusts, always hopes, always perseveres" 1 Corinthians 13:4-7 NIV.

In 1 Corinthians 13, the chapter right before 14 that people use to silence women, Paul did not waver from the goal of his letter, which was to emphasize the need to minister in love. The law of love should govern all aspects of a Christian's life, but especially _____.

Love is patient and kind, it does not envy or boast. It does not _____others, it is not self-seeking...Love does not demand its own way!

Love is _____ and allows others adequate time to share what God has placed on their hearts.

Love is kind and _____ the contributions others make to the ministry of the church.

Love doesn't _____ or give way to the natural insecurities in our hearts. It honors without fearing others might get more than we do - responding to their ministry in a way that would build them up to bring them even greater ministry through their lives.

Love does not boast and is not proud; it doesn't think of _____ (or at least it fights the instincts to consider the ways, thoughts and inclinations of self).

Love does not dishonor either _____ or men who are sharing their heart by interrupting them while they are sharing.

Love puts _____ first, and seeks to draw the best from them.

Love is not self-seeking, it does not demand or _____, but encourages. Love protects, esteems and builds up.

It does not target one sex and demean them in the name of God, reducing their life's meaning to a subservient, underprivileged human. Love _____ their equality and strives to convince them of their worth and value in Christianity in whatever capacity God calls them to.

Love protects the humanity of women!

Equal Humanity for Women

2. I've heard people say they love and respect women, but do not believe they should be in ministry because they are not equal to a man.

So, I ask you:

Do you feel loved by that way of thinking?

Does it build your confidence?

Or encourage you in the Father's love for you?

If someone respects or loves you they will see you as equal to themselves. We are all one in Christ!

I've seen people so flippantly _____women and reduce them to subhumans that God wants to punish. Yet, God said in Genesis 1:27, "God created human beings in his own image. In the image of God he created them; male and female he created them."

God made both _____and _____in His likeness. He created both sexes on purpose, it was no accident you were made a woman - God is delighted you are a woman.

If someone says you are subhuman or second-class, then they are saying _____is second-class, because you were made in HIS image!

If someone thinks women are anything less than the wonderful work of _____they are, they are insulting God, because He made us. We are His creation and His delight!

You mean so much to Him, because you are the expression of His _____toward mankind!

Our _____cannot be defined by mere opinion, because opinions are unreliable and change constantly. Our humanity is a gift from God and His Word says we are equal.

Do you believe the pain and injustices of prejudice reduce your value in God's eyes?

Robbing the Church

3. The harvest is plentiful and the Father needs laborers. Isn't it time we take the limits off women so we can work together to bring in the Harvest?

"The harvest is plentiful, but the workers are few. Ask the Lord of the Harvest, therefore, to send out workers into his field" Luke 10:2.

_____is NOT a gender specific Scripture. We need all races and genders to fulfill the mandate the Lord has given us!

Truly, as a church, we are not being very intelligent. By buying into this scheme, we have robbed ourselves of _____our labor force, simply because we have fallen prey to personal bias and religious bigotry.

Sexism is however a smart strategy for the kingdom of
_____ to use in attempting to stop the spread of the gospel.
The harvest field is ready and now, truly, more than ever we need laborers—it's time
to reassess our imposed qualifications for ministry.

Learning to Minister

4. Realizing the confusion in the new church, Paul attempted to bring clarification and
guidance to the early Christians.

Paul answers by saying first in, "*Women should be silent during the church meetings.
It is not proper for them to speak. They should be submissive, just as the law says*" (1
Corinthians 14:34 NLT).

It sounds like Paul is unsaying what he had said previously, which was to see women
released in the churches (see 1 Corinthians 14:1 & 39, Romans 16:1-2, 1 Timothy 2:9).
Was Paul telling women not to preach?

If we compare this verse to his previous statements about _____
and _____, we can see that he wasn't meaning for women to be
silent in church and never to speak again. But just as with prophesy, his "be silent"
from the Greek word hésuchazó meaning: rest from work, cease from altercation, am
silent, live quietly or lead a quiet life, was a guide to heart behavior.

This lines up with what he said previously in 1 Corinthians 14:26-33 to be silent (be
still) while others are speaking and wait your turn. So it is not
_____ and everyone is benefited by what you have to say.

In 1 Corinthians 14, Paul was requiring both men and women to have a
_____ heart-attitude toward everyone in their meetings, not
to fight and try to be heard above everyone else.

In order to display _____for one another, he wanted them to develop a gentle, submissive attitude toward one another, preferring the other above themselves (Romans 12:10).

"Do nothing out of selfish ambition or vain conceit. Rather, in humility value others above yourselves" (Philippians 2:3 NIV).

His attitude of rest teaching reinforces his instructions on possessing and ministering with an attitude of submission. Paul is _____ what he said earlier: that women should continue ministering in an attitude of submission. As he stated in Ephesian 5:21, they should all "submit to one another" or be subject to one another.

He is not saying women alone should submit to the law, but women should be taught to submit to the same law men do, which is the law of _____.

Because Paul talks about husbands directly after this line, many people believe he's commanding women to submit to their husbands. But if you read it in line with the rest of chapter 14, it would be submission to other _____, not specifically to men.

The _____ Jews who wrote the Septuagint (the Greek version of the Hebrew Scriptures), used the word submission as a parallel for being silent before God. They used the word to imply that one should submit oneself to God first and foremost above any human being. Their first rule was to surrender to the leading and guidance of God, therefore submitting and relinquishing their lives to Him.

The focus of Paul's letter was to reinforce the law of love that was first established as the new commandment (John 13:34), and took precedence over every other teaching. So, here we see again Paul simply restating what he said previously in the letter that _____is the most important law and should come first in ministry.

Women, as well as men, are commanded to attain an _____
of submission as the law of love requires (Ephesians 5:21). Submitting first to God,
then submitting to others as unto God.

Another misunderstanding about this Scripture has risen in the church, simply
because few people truly understand the meaning of submission. The word hypotássō
is best translated as yielding voluntarily—it is a choice. And hupakoé literally means
"submission to what is heard," not to be a _____only, but a
doer as well.

By yielding to others and considering them before ourselves we choose to act in
humility and God gives His grace to the _____, both male
or female.

An Emotional Rebuttal

5. Paul wrestled in earnest with the misogynistic teachings of his times and, yes, he
defended women.

He is quoted as saying, "*Women should be silent during the church meetings. It is not
proper for them to speak. They should be submissive, just as the law says. If they have
any questions, they should ask their husbands at home, for it is improper for women
to speak in church meetings.*

*"Or do you think God's word originated with you Corinthians? Are you the only ones
to whom it was given? If you claim to be a prophet or think you are spiritual, you
should recognize that what I am saying is a command from the Lord himself. But if
you do not recognize this, you yourself will be not recognized."*

But then he says, "*So, my dear brothers and sisters, be eager to prophesy and don't forbid speaking in tongues. But be sure that everything is done properly and in order*" 1 Corinthians 14:34-40 NLT.

What we must understand about this passage is in Paul's time there were _____ in writing, so, we don't really know when one thought ends and another begins.

At the end of verse 35, it states that it is a "disgraceful" thing for women to speak in church. Which makes it sound like he doesn't want them to preach. Yet, there is a small word right after it which is what they call an emotional _____ for what was just said—indicating a counterargument or refutation.

Paul was quoting a teaching that was not his own, such as "*It is disgraceful for a women to speak in church*" (1 Corinthians 14:35 NIV). Then he answered what he had quoted with an emotional rebuttal, arguing against it saying, "It is disgraceful (or improper) for women to speak in church? Nonsense!" or "What?" or "No way!"

Then he states the opposite of the quote he just stated which is, "*Do you think the word of God originated with you?*" Here he has another emotional rebuttal, such as "What!" So, it may read "What! Are you the only people it has reached?"

Similarly, if you wanted to quote something you disagreed with like, "Pigs can fly," and then said, "Phewy," there's just no way to translate it. So, Paul's emotional rebuttal has been simply _____ of translations for centuries.

In this letter, Paul quoted others, such as the Old Testament Scriptures, the words of Jesus (Luke 22:19-20), the Greek dramatist Menander (Thais), rabbinic prophesy (B. Makkot 23a) and other believers (1 Corinthians 1:12, 3:4, 6:12-13, 10:23, 12:3, 15:35) and non-believers (1 Corinthians 10:28, 12:3, 14:25).

That, together with his use of the mark indicating an emotional rebuttal, show that he is _____ contradicting his previous teaching on the release of women into ministry positions (1 Corinthians 14:26; also Romans 16:1), but actually reiterating it.

After voicing his rebuttal of the quoted concepts, he concludes this thought by _____ his conclusions in verse 39 that both men and women were to prophesy. He says, *"So, my dear brothers and sisters, be eager to prophesy, and don't forbid speaking in tongues. But (or just) be sure that everything is done properly and in order"* (1 Corinthians 14:39-40).

Things to ponder:

Of all the characteristics the Father possesses, love defines Him best. If He is love, do you believe He would want you to feel unloved and undervalued?

Does the great commission include you?

God is your defense! He will make your innocence shine like the dawn!

Daily Devotions:

Do you believe the pain and injustices of prejudice reduce your value in God's eyes?

List two incidents where you have believed the prejudices against you:

1.

2.

Putting on the whole armor of God means to put on love. *"A final word: Be strong in the Lord and in his mighty power. Put on all of God's armor so that you will be able to stand firm against all strategies of the devil"* Ephesians 6:10. The mighty power of God is LOVE! Soak in His love and let it cover you, revealing all the hidden areas of your heart that need His restoring power.

Through this Scripture, describe how you believe God sees you:

LESSON NINE

Removing the Restraints

Who do you believe can remove your restraints and restore your value?
(Circle One)

You ◆ Friends ◆ Family ◆ Spouse ◆ Father God

Your Father anticipate the day when you will walk in freedom and JOY!

(Answers to study guide questions are in the back of the book)

Trouble in Ephesus

1. Paul dealt with the errors that had crept into the church in Ephesus in his letter to Timothy, dark and wicked ideologies had attacked the church from without and from within.

The Ephesian church is one which Paul had started with a woman named
_____ and her husband Aquila, but the church was now being overrun by the witchcraft, pagan worship and _____ that pervaded the city.

Some believers taught twisted truths, mixing Christianity with other
_____ _____amongst the Lord's people. There was no local church building, but believers met in homes. Timothy was _____the only teacher.

Paul tells Timothy to "*Cling to your faith in Christ, and keep your conscience clear. For some people have deliberately violated their consciences; as a result their faith has been shipwrecked*" 1 Timothy 1:19.

The widespread beliefs of the pagans were so infectious that Paul was urgent in his letter to Timothy telling him to "_____!" as if he were in jeopardy of falling prey to the erroneous teachings in the city.

Then Paul continues in 1 Timothy 2:1-4 saying, "*I urge you, first of all, to pray for all people. Ask God to help them; interceded on their behalf, and give thanks for them. Pray this way for kings and all who are in authority so that we can live peaceful and quiet lives marked by godliness and dignity. This is good and pleases God our Savior, who wants everyone to be saved and to understand truth.*"

Paul wants Timothy to _____the people to _____for those caught in darkness. Paul urges them to have mercy for those who were caught in error, and remind them to pray, because God wants to save everyone (v. 4).

In 1 Timothy 2:8, Paul told the men not to _____or _____, but to have mercy and pray for those lost in deception. In debating, they had lost the focus of their witness, which is love and tried to accomplish the work of the Spirit with human anger (James 1:20).

Harsh Language or Redemptive Teaching

2. 1 Timothy 2 seems to have the harshest anti-women language in the Bible and is a difficult passage to study, but with further study we find a much different truth than what has historically been presented to us.

The NIV reads: "*Therefore I want the men everywhere to pray, lifting up holy hands without anger or disputing. I also want the women to dress modestly, with decency and propriety, adorning themselves, not with elaborate hairstyles or gold or pearls or expensive clothes, but with good deeds, appropriate for women who profess to worship God.*
"*A woman should learn in quietness and full submission. I do not permit a woman to teach or to assume authority over a man; she must be quiet. For Adam was formed*

first, then Eve. And Adam was not the one deceived; it was the woman who was deceived and became a sinner. But women will be saved through childbearing—if they continue in faith, love and holiness with propriety." 1 Timothy 2:8-15.

Now read the difference as presented by David J. Hamilton, a Biblical scholar who wrote his master's thesis on these passages from his book, *Why Not Women*, written in accordance with the original Greek translation, and changes chosen to reflect the Greek grammar more accurately: *"I want men everywhere to lift up holy hands in prayer, without anger or disputing. Likewise, I want women to dress modestly, with decency and propriety, not with braided hair or gold or pearls or expensive clothes, but with good deeds, appropriate for women who profess to worship God.*

"A woman should learn in quietness and full submission. I do not permit a woman to teach or to have authority over a man; she must be silent. For Adam was formed first, then Eve. And Adam was not the one deceived; it was the woman who was deceived and became a sinner. But she will be saved through the childbearing"
1 Timothy 2:8-15.

Virtually the same passage of Scripture, with only a few changes, made it much less devastating to women.

Was Paul telling Timothy to STOP women from preaching because they were too easily deceived? Paul the champion for mercy, who'd established this very church with the help of Priscilla a woman he greatly esteem? _____.

In 1 Timothy 2:9-10 Paul turns to the women of Ephesus and says
"_____" or "_____."

Paul's first word was likewise, which in the Greek is represented by an ellipsis, a literary equal sign.

So Paul was telling them that everything he had just said to the men was now applied to women and then he added, *"I want women to dress modestly, with decency and propriety, not with braided hair or gold or pearls or expensive clothes but with good deeds, appropriate for women who _____ to worship God."*

The pagan worship in the city of Ephesus was livid with _____, and Paul did not want Christian women to be associated with the promiscuous, pagan women.

The important part of this Scripture was that Paul was telling them how to dress, while they _____ or shared their Christian beliefs. It was understood that Christian women were sharing their faith.

Paul used the gender _____ term anthropos consistently when referring to Christians ministering and winning souls, because he wanted every warrior he could get his hands on!

Paul did not excluded women in or outside the church from sharing or teaching if they were qualified teachers, because he needed laborers.

False Teacher

3. In 1 Timothy 2:11-15, Paul talks about an unnamed woman in the church who had been deceived by the false doctrine spreading through Ephesus. Although, she was in the church, her teachings were most likely a mixture of the cultural pagan beliefs and Christianity; a twisted version of the truth that Paul felt was detrimental to the believers there.

Writing to Timothy he says, "A woman should learn in quietness and full submission. I do not permit a woman to teach or to have authority over a man; she must be silent. For Adam was formed first, then Eve. And Adam was not the one deceived; it was the woman who was deceived and became a sinner. But she will be save through the childbearing." 1 Timothy 2:11-15.

Paul was not addressing these comments to ALL women in Ephesus, but just ONE woman. We know this because in verses 11-15 all the plural nouns are gone, he stopped speaking in generalities, "everyone, men, women" and changed to a singular noun, a woman. Everywhere else, when speaking of women he says _____ (plural) but here he changes to the singular use of a _____ (singular).

Paul chooses not to name the woman who was caught up in deception, because he hopes to win her over to right theology. Paul wanted to take her from _____to the _____. He says in v.11, she (the woman he mentioned) "should learn in quietness and full submission," Paul wanted this woman taught correctly.

He wanted this ONE women to be taught and Paul further instructed her to learn in quietness and _____; quiet meaning a teachable attitude, complying and fully submitting with the instructions given her.

When Paul says, "I do not permit a woman to teach," he is saying that in regards to the _____woman who was teaching erroneously, because she was not yet qualified.

Paul's ultimate goal for this woman was to make her a qualified _____for the truth, that was his goal, not to silence her permanently, just until she was qualified or had learned the truth.

Jewish scholars always connected learning with teaching, the latter being the end result of learning. Otherwise, what was the use of _____them.

Earlier Paul told Timothy to remember the teachings of his grandmother, Lois, and his mother, Eunice, who Paul knew to be great teachers of the way, in order to guide him through the deception he was encountering in Ephesus. Do you think that he had changed his mind and was now forbidding all women from teaching?

Cultural Differences

4. In the early church, there were no public church buildings at this time. All teachings were done in homes or outside in secret places. People would gather together and basically have a Bible study without a Bible. Teachers taught from what they had learnt.

Most likely, Lois and Eunice trained Timothy in the way of salvation in their
_____ (1 Timothy 4:6).

Women were the care-takers of the home and were opening up their homes for Christians to meet together and share. That makes it seem more
_____that they were being told not to speak in their own homes.

When Paul says, "I do not permit a woman to teach or to have authority over a man," again, he was talking about the same _____, that she should not be allowed to have authority.

The words "to have authority" are murky and difficult to translate, because they were so seldom used in the new testament and are difficult to reference. But they were only referring to the one _____who was in error.

Then Paul mentions _____ and says, "For Adam was formed first, then Eve. And Adam was not the one deceived; it was the woman who was deceived and became a sinner" 1 Timothy 2: 13-14.

Paul had compassion for Eve and did not bring up the fall to
_____ women, but to explain that Eve, unlike Adam, was deceived. He believed she had been deceived because she was not adequately

_____ what God had said to Adam in Genesis 3:6.

He was not saying that, because Eve was deceived all women were more easily _____ and should not become teachers. He was saying that because Eve was not taught well, and women were banned from learning, they were vulnerable to making errors in their teaching. His solution was to _____ them!

Paul was most likely refuting a false doctrine circulating at the time in Ephesus. An exaggerated version of creation which taught that women were the _____ of men and were, therefore, head or ruler over them. In referencing the fall, he may have been addressing the teaching this _____ woman had circulated.

By saying "Adam was formed first, then Eve," he wasn't saying men were better or smarter, but was just refuting a false doctrine that had been spreading. He wanted to bring truth, not create a flip-flop of error in the other direction.

Will Your Babies Save YOU?

5. In 1 Timothy 2: 14 Paul says, *"But she will be save through the childbearing,"* He did not mean our baby- making would save us, as if that was the only thing we are good for. He was not referring to childbearing, because he did not say "childbearing" but "the childbearing."

Timothy _____ what Paul referred to so Paul did not need to define what he meant when he said it. He was referring to THE CHILD - the Christ child in Genesis 3:15.

The childbearing was a reference to God's promised _____.
"I will put enmity between you [the serpent] and the woman, and between and hers;

he will crush your head, and you will strike his heel." God's plan of salvation.

All women, as well as all men, will be saved through Genesis 3:15, which is the plan of salvation, not _____.

The _____ of the woman, Christ, would bring about the destruction of Satan. The woman Eve, and all women, would bring Satan's downfall!

The woman Satan had _____ would bring truth into the world, it would be she who would be the vessel heaven would use to overtake the rule of the prince of darkness. The victory of her seed was the vengeance of the woman - her victory over her deceiver, her justification.

Paul was asking for the same compassion for this ONE woman who had been deceived, because she needed salvation. Remember, Paul, above all things, was a soul-winner. He wanted her saved, not silence!

Women Leaders

6. 1 Timothy 3:1-13 continues to bring a message of equality for both genders. Paul says "*If someone (anyone) aspires to be an elder, he (or she) desires an honorable position*" (emphasis added) then he gives a lengthy list of qualifications for elders in the church. He didn't want new believers teaching because they might fall into the same deception as the ONE woman he'd just referenced.

The important verses in chapter 3 are 11-13, in which Paul says, likewise (or, in the same way), women should be held by the same _____ as the men which he'd just mentioned, before becoming leaders and teachers in the church.

The word for women Paul used in the Greek was "gune," which can be translated as either wives or women. If translated wives, it slants the meaning, making it sound like Paul was only referring to the wives of the ministers, not women ministers.

Paul wrote gune and meant it to mean _____. We know this, because Paul consistently used the gender inclusive terms when writing to churches, referring constantly to Christians of both genders which is consistent with the rest of his behavior towards women.

If Paul wanted to _____women ministers, why in 1 Timothy 3:11-13 would he set up guidelines for women ministers?

Remember:

We have to remember that Paul spent a great deal of time with the churches he started. The vast majority of what he taught them was in verbal form and we can never know everything he taught them. We have only his written letters which give us just a taste of what he taught. In much of the letters he refers to what he's taught them audibly when he was with them. He references it knowing that they already had an understanding of what he was communicating. He didn't give an in depth explanation, because they already had an understanding of what he is implying.

In understanding Paul's letters, we have to keep in mind his actions as well, and compare them with what he wrote. It is wrong to assume we know what he meant and erase his character with a few verses he wrote, it's wrong to him as well as to those it effects. To be fair, we need to dig deep and embrace the full meaning of what was said. If we don't, we are no better than the false teachers Paul is referring to in his letters.

"Pursue righteousness and a godly life, along with faith, love, perseverance, and gentleness. Fight the good fight for the true faith" 1 Timothy 6:11-12 NLT.

Things to ponder:

Do you think Paul is trying to silence women ministers?

If he was, why do you think he gave guidelines for women in ministry?

Did Paul appreciate the ministry of women ministers?

Daily Devotions

What do you believe Paul was trying to do for the church of Ephesus?

List two incidents where you have felt you should not share about the Lord because you're a woman:

1.

2.

Jesus is coming soon and laborers are needed. That day when Cassandra received her crown, I thought of the scripture in, *"I am coming soon. Hold on to what you have, so that no one will take your crown. The one who is victorious I will make a pillar in the temple of my God"* Revelation 3:11-12 NIV. Pursue the righteousness that only God gives, persevere in your faith that God wants to use your life to share His Gospel with faith, love a, perseverance, and gentleness. Fight the good fight for the true faith. 1 Timothy 6:11-12 NLT.

Through these Scriptures, describe how you believe God sees you:

LESSON TEN

Army of Women

Who do you believe understands just how powerful you really are?
(Circle One)

You ◆ Friends ◆ Family ◆ Spouse ◆ Father God

God the Father sees the hidden potential inside you and He is contending for your destiny!

(Answers to study guide questions are in the back of the book)

Be sure to read the visions in God's Magnum Opus: The Value of a Woman that go along with this teaching.

Hidden Potential

1. You do have potential hidden inside of you; you are capable of much more than you know. God will fight an army of doubt to see you realize your potential.

"The Lord announces the word [Divine utterance], and the women who proclaim it are a mighty throng: 'Kings and armies flee in haste; the women at home divide the plunder!'" Psalm 68:11-12 NIV (emphasis mine).

You can tell all those anti-women people who quote passages of Scripture as proof that women should not minister: Please read the whole Bible!

If you read only those verses, you may agree with those who've used the Bible to keep women from walking in_____ to their callings, but you can never or should never read one verse without taking into consideration all the verses before and after it. Nor should you use one verse to negate the rest of the _____, in which we are given countless examples of

68

powerful women ministers.

Find the Scripture reference for each mighty woman:

Miriam, the sister of Moses in _____, was a prophet of God and led the tribes of Israel.

Deborah, the wife of Lappidoth in _____, was a prophet of God and ruled the nation of Israel!

Jael, the wife of Heber the Kenite in _____, was a warrior of God who saved the armies of Israel with a tent peg!

Rahab, the prostitute, hid the messengers of Israel in _____.

Huldah, the wife of Shullum in _____, was a prophet of God!

Queen Esther in _____saved the nation of Israel!

Anna, the daughter of Phanuel, a prophet of God, in _____, prophesied the coming of the Christ child.

Mary Magdalene, Joanna, and Susanna in _____followed Jesus.

Martha and Mary, the sisters of Lazarus, in _____followed Jesus.

The Samaritan woman at the well in _____ started a revival.

Elizabeth, the wife of Zechariah, prophesied to Mary the mother of Jesus in _____.

Mary, the wife of Joseph, the mother of the Savior, prophesied in _____.

Tabitha, in _____, was raised to life by Peter. She was so good to so many doing many charitable acts, the people couldn't let her go

Lydia in Acts 16:13-15, Pheobe a woman deacon in Romans 16:1, Priscilla who discipled Paul in Romans 16:3 ; Junia, a woman apostle in Romans 16:7, Lois and Eunice, the mother and grandmother of Timothy were praised by Paul for being strong women of faith in 2 Timothy 1:5, just to name a few.

This list is very small, because through the centuries and in the culture of middle-east women were not counted. They were seen as unimportant, so were rarely mentioned. However, God has seen and knows the history of every woman He created and is continuously grateful for the work His daughters have done and will do for His kingdom. He will never forget you!

God Will Bring the Victory to YOU!

2. The enemy has tried to limit the effectiveness of women, but, just like Jael in Judges 4:17-24, if the enemy keeps you from going to war, God will bring the victory to you.

If the enemy has _____ you, use it to your advantage. By underestimating you, he's placed you in just the right position to ruin him.

In Judges 4, Deborah was a prophet who governed the entire nation of Israel while Sisera lead King Jabin's army against Israel. One day, she called for Barak to lead the armies of _____ in battle against the Canaanite king.

She said to him, "*This is what the Lord, the God of Israel, commands you: Call out 10,000 warriors from the tribes of Naphtali and Zebulun at Mount Tabor. And I will call out Sisera, commander of Jabin's army, along with his chariots and warriors, to the Kishon River. There I will give you victory over him.*" (Judges 4:6-7 NLT).

Barak refused to go against Sisera unless _____ agreed to go with him (Judges 4:8). Deborah agreed to go with the army, but prophesied that because of his lack of faith, he would receive no honor from the victory God would give them. Instead, she said, "*The Lord's victory over Sisera will be at the hands of a woman*" (Judges 4:9 NLT).

"*Jael, the wife of Heber, was at _____ in her tent, but God chose to raise her up to be His warrior! If she couldn't go to war, He would bring the battle to her.*

When Barak attacked, God caused Sisera and his men to run in panic. _____ ran to the tent of Jael and she went out to meet him saying, 'Come into my tent, sir. Come in. Don't be afraid.' So he went into her tent, and she covered him with a blanket.

'Please give me some water,' he said. 'I'm thirsty.' So she gave him some _____ from a leather bag and covered him again.

'Stand at the door of the _____,' he told her. 'If anybody comes and asks you if there is anyone here, say no.'

But when Sisera fell asleep from exhaustion, Jael quietly crept up to him with a
_____*and* _____*in her hand.*
Then she drove the tent peg through his temple and into the ground, and so he died.

When Barak came looking for Sisera, Jael went out to meet him. She said, 'Come, and I will show you the man you are looking for.' So he followed her into the tent and found Sisera lying there dead, with the tent peg through his
_____'''* (Judges 4:17-22 NLT).

_____was probably the last one that Barak considered would win the battle for Israel that day, but God chose her for that very reason.

God was sending us a message: We cannot limit Him! He refuses to be put in a box! Tell Him He can't do something and that is just what He will do. Give Him a desert and He'll make a forest (Isaiah 41:19).

Give Him a housewife and He'll make her a _____. This is God's heart concerning you. He sees beyond your weaknesses and sees a victorious warrior.

Victorious Women in Revivals

3. Every major revival in history had women at the forefront!

In the Welsh revival of 1905, revivalist Evan Roberts, allowed women to lead in the services he held. These women were breaking new ground just by
_____and _____. They labored in prayer with Roberts to see the manifestation of God's presence.

_____led men and women, both black and white, from all ranks of society in the Azuza Street revival from 1906-1909. He was discipled by a woman as well as recognized the great strength women brought to the throngs of hungry, passionate seekers who saw heaven come down in the little chapel in Los Angeles, CA.

In both the first and second great awakenings, women labored and interceded to bring in the _____.

The Second Great Awakening especially effected the lives of women. The majority of people converted were _____who also played a crucial role in the awakening's advancement and direction. Many husbands actually demanded their wives choose between their religious activities and their

_____.

Revivalist Charles Finney recognized the power of women's _____ and knew their role in the revival was crucial. He often called upon women to lead in prayer publicly. He saw that without the role of _____, it would have been much harder for the revival's effectiveness to be realized.

The Second Great Awakening (1825-1835) produced many _____ movements that continued to develop for centuries to come. Many prominent and well-informed female-led organizations responsible for many of the evangelical convert, were birthed through the awakening.

These women-led organizations propelled the movement's focus toward social _____and _____. Of these, the American Bible Society and the Temperance Movement were the most well-known.

Most notably, the Second Great Awakening birthed the movement for women's rights, as well as the abolitionist movement. These movements were founded on belief in the _____—that all men, as well as all women, were created equally by God!

Beguines Women

4. The courage of the Beguines women in the thirteenth century is remarkable. In Northern Europe during the middle ages, the brave Beguines women fought against prejudice and broke the mold for women.

During this time in history, women were allowed only two honorable roles in society in which they could serve God: becoming a _____or running a household as a _____. Joining a convent to serve as a nun was very expensive and there was no other way for a woman to serve God.

Forming communities of women vowing to live a consecrated life to God, they performed good works and took care of each other. These women devoted their lives to _____and serving the poor.

Their communities flourished as they sought an _____ relationship with God and devoted themselves to religious work. Before long, men as well as women sought out these communities to sit under the powerful teachings of Beguines women.

One of the movement's leaders was Marie of Oignies, who had visionary encounters, experienced _____ (a sudden change in perception due to direct contact with Holy Spirit) and wept uncontrollably as she reflected on the crucifixion of Christ.

When the movement shifted toward Christian mysticism, which was a move toward the Spirit, _____and visions in the communities, they began to experience greater persecution by the church.

Marguerite Porete, a French Beguine Christian-mystic, was accused of heresy by the Catholic church and burned at the stake in 1310 in Paris. Her book, The Mirror of Simple Souls, was censured as _____and, failing to recant its teachings, she was condemned to die.

They came under heavy religious _____by the Pope, the
bishops and the inquisition until their numbers began to wane by the 17th century.

Through the 1200s-1600s the Beguines revival spread across Belgium, the
Netherlands, Northern France and Germany. And with a focus on intimacy with
Christ, the effect they accomplished was evident by the wide-spread renewal amongst
the middle-class.

A Harvest of Potential

5. The Father gets great joy in seeing you walk in the fullness of your potential. When
He called you out of your shell to do the greater works (John 14:12), He called forth
potential in your spirit-man to accomplish His will.

Heavenly potential you've never realized is already inside you waiting to be
_____—to birth your dreams and manifest God's presence.

God sees the _____the enemy has sown in your heart much
more clearly than you do, so He calls your attention to it so you can uproot it.

The reality is, there is a war in the _____over possession of
your heart and mind. When you battle with the lies of the enemy, you will begin to see
the realization of your potential.

It is _____to heaven and so very necessary to the earth—
you are that important. As you take authority over the lies of the enemy that want to
rob you of your confidence, know you are not just wrestling for your own sake, but
for the triumph of the kingdom of heaven.

As you stand in confidence to defeat destiny's thief, understand and recognize you stand in the confidence of the _____kingdom of heaven.

So, tell that devil he has no chance against you and refuse to give him any place in your life. Submit to God and the devil WILL FLEE from you (James 4:7).

"He who began a good work in you will carry it on to completion until the day of Christ Jesus" (Philippians 1:6 NIV).

Psalm 68:11 prophesied the coming of a great army of women who would experience incredible victories for the Kingdom of Christ. God is calling His warrior-women to all areas of service in His kingdom.

Truly, He's prepared you and now He's calling you. He needs _____. The harvest is waiting—will you come?

Things to ponder:

If you deposited potential inside creation, would it grieve you to see that potential denied?

If you were the Father, would it delight you to see hidden potential drawn out?

If God displayed his power through a woman in the Old testament, making Deborah judge and prophet over the nation of Israel, does it seem silly to you that in the New Testament, which is governed by grace, that power would be denied women?

Daily Devotions:

Whose truth are you believing about yourself?

List two incidents where you have believed wrongly about yourself:

1.

2.

Make Father God your mirror. "*Every good and perfect gift is from above, coming down from the Father of the heavenly lights, who does not change like shifting shadows*" James 1:17; Romans 16:25; 2 Corinthians 5:17. You are a good and perfect gift sent from the Father - you are God's magnum opus. Think about how carefully He's designed you (Psalm 139:13-14). Thank Father God for making you so perfectly; thank Him for His commitment to you.

Through these Scriptures, describe how you believe God sees you:

It Will Not Be Taken From Her

Now who do you believe knows the real truth about your value?
(Circle One)

You ◆ Friends ◆ Family ◆ Spouse ◆ Father God

Truly, there is only ONE version of the truth about your worth and that is the Father's truth.

(Answers to study guide questions are in the back of the book)

Sexism is a Trap

1. Like racism or any other measure of hatred, sexism is a trap set for humanity by the one who hates the most. Satan is determined to divide us and he has been successful, but not for much longer.

"The Lord detests double standards of every kind..." Proverbs 20:10 NLT.

Many have twisted the Scriptures to cause _____ in an effort to strengthen the divide between the genders, continuing this divisive teaching of the enemy.

Some believe that God is male, because He calls Himself our Father, proving men are superior. But God also refers to Himself as a mother, can you find the references?

_____states women were made in His likeness.

In _____, God refers to His womb.

_____, the servant of the Lord refers to God as a woman in labor.

In _____, God refers to Himself as a pregnant woman.

The most compelling scripture about God our "mother" is
_____. The Lord says, *"As a mother comforts her child, so will I comfort you; and you will be comforted over Jerusalem"* (NIV).

God is not male or female in the physical, but He is _____.
And He has both male and female characteristics. It is our spirits, not our physical bodies, that are made in His image.

The church has given men a sense of _____. But is that what they really want?

Some _____ for their sexist agenda vehemently, but what do they get out of it? Just the fleeting feeling of a favorable position - that's all.

God is drawing nearer and nearer to the humble, to those they attack with their discrimination. If our hearts are pure and we are truly seeking to know God, we should be looking for ways to _____ourselves, running away from anything that could cause us to puff ourselves up.

It's important that men stand up and fight for the equality of women as for their own soul. By accepting even a _____between the genders, men make themselves superior to women and, in essence, fight against the plans of God being manifested in the lives of countless generations of women.

Husbands, fathers and brothers, can be mighty warriors for God, by fighting against the enemy's _____ (Genesis 3:15), fighting as if the kingdom depends on it.

None of us want to find ourselves fighting _____our Father's kingdom. We must determine not to hand down a morsel of traditional disdain to our daughters.

We must ask our men to stand and declare with us, "Not my daughters! My children, and especially my daughters, will know who they are in Christ and not be limited by the error of mankind."

Our daughters are His daughters!

Oppressive Expectations

2. We have received an inheritance of oppressive, unreachable expectations through the ideologies of the traditional roles in the family.

I feel just as bad for the heavy weight men feel they must carry for the family; they were not meant to carry this weight alone. We were meant to be _____ partners in marriage and family in Christ!

Men and women both tend to find their value in how they perform the _____family roles, but Christ showed us a better way. He wants us to find our worth in following Him!

Women are also sexist towards each other and themselves, because they hold tight to the traditions of generations. Is it possible to teach others what we do not know ourselves?

Our traditional family values are only _____ if they line up with what Jesus taught us. If they become a bondage and a snare, they are working for the enemy and against us.

In Luke 8:21, Jesus redefines who the family unit is, *"Now Jesus' mother and brothers came to see him, but they were not able to get near him because of the crowd. Someone told him, 'Your mother and brothers are standing outside, wanting to see you.' He replied, 'My mother and brothers are those who hear God's word and put it into practice.'"* Luke 8:19-21 NIV.

Christ wants us to know that above all else, we are all His children if we follow His leading. Whether we are man or woman, we are just as _____ and just as loved by the Father.

In following Christ and doing the will of the Father, we are _____ to serve Him. The only qualification for the family of God is Luke 8:21.

Mary OR Martha

3. The Lord spoke to me years ago, "Victoria, you can be a Mary or a Martha, but you can't be both."

Mary and Martha were two sisters who followed Jesus and were discipled by His ministry. Jesus was obviously very good friends with both sisters, but Mary seemed to have a better _____ of what He expected from her.

Martha felt that preparing a meal for Jesus was more _____ and was upset by Mary's refusal to help her prepare it. Their struggle created an opportunity for Jesus to give them both instruction on what He truly desired from them.

Mary put her _____with Jesus ahead of the expectations of society, but Martha did not.

She was caught up in maintaining her role as the dutiful, ideal Jewish woman. Not only did she feel strongly about her opinion of the proper _____ of women in the home, but she demanded that Jesus scold Mary for not doing it with her. He refused (Luke 10:38-40).

"'Martha, Martha,' the Lord answered, 'you are worried and upset about many things, but few things are needed—or indeed only one. Mary has chosen what is better, and it will not be taken away from her'" Luke 10:41-42 NIV.

It seems like Jesus did not understand our rules! No, He was very clear; Mary had chosen to become His disciple - it was her _____. Jesus protected Mary's right to choose!

_____have a choice in how they live their lives. It gives God pleasure when we walk with Him and fulfill the calling on our life. As women, we represent Him well as we follow the leading of His Spirit.

When God told me I could choose either to be a Mary or a Martha, He was developing in me the recognition of my right to choose and not letting the ideas and ideologies of others dictate my life.

God wants you to know you have a choice and what you choose should not be determined by society. It is _____choice, not theirs.

He wants you to choose! Will you follow Him or mankind? So I say to you, sisters: You can be a Mary or you can be a Martha, but you can't be both!

Blessed Rather

4. Jesus amazed another woman in Luke 11:27-28, who received a compelling challenge from Him.

"A woman in the crowd called out to Jesus, 'Blessed is the mother who gave you birth and nursed you.' But He answered back, 'Blessed rather are those who hear the word of God and obey it'" Luke 11:27-28 NIV.

She defined her worth through the lives of the children she bore, which was the traditional _____ of a woman's value in society.

Jesus revolutionized the way _____ thought about themselves. He challenged women to reconsider who they were and what they were created for.

Jesus did not think motherhood was a _____ thing, but His response indicates there was more going on with the woman's comment. He answered her and said, *"Blessed rather are those who hear the word of God and obey it."*

Jesus redefined her worth and gave her a choice!

Women were told their only _____ was in having babies, so women naturally defined their worth by their children. Jesus was trying to get her to correct her vision of herself. He wanted her to value herself, not by her role as a mother, but by living for Him.

No Apologies

5. Do not grieve the Spirit by apologizing for the calling on your life. Do not grieve

Him by making excuses for being a woman. God is proud of His daughters.

Some women in ministry say things like, "A man was given my anointing first, but he didn't want it, so it fell to me." Does that make sense?

If God wanted a _____to have your anointing, He could surely find another man who would take it. God wanted to give the anointing and calling to you because you were His first choice.

Never apologize for your _____, it grieves Him. He knew you were a woman when He called you, and for that reason you are perfect for the calling He has for you!

We women tend to apologize for our giftings and callings, because we feel the _____of a society that has yet to embrace the kingdom of heaven's value system.

As women who _____our Father God, we need to ask ourselves: Should we bow to culture or our God?

Will you fear more the chastisement of those who think women should remain silent, or become what heaven would like you to become?

The Word of God in Luke 11:36 says, "Therefore, if your whole body is full of light, and no part of it dark, it will be just as full of light as when a lamp shines its light on you" (NIV). The body of Christ will not shine with the true light of heaven until we are whole and every part of us is lit up and brightly shining as one.

Hold On to What You Have

6. Our struggles equip us for the battles that lay ahead of us and *"when troubles come*

your way, consider it an opportunity for great joy. For you know that when your faith is tested, your endurance has a chance to grow. So let it grow, for when your endurance is fully developed, you will be perfect and complete, needing nothing" (James 1:2-4 NLT).

Hold on to what you have! Use every _____ to strengthen your witness for His blessed kingdom. He looks on you with great pleasure and pride. He's confident in your future and loves to recall the victories you've experienced.

Your victory brings great joy to heaven! You will become a pillar in His temple!

Revelation 3:10-12 says, *"Since you have kept my command to endure patiently, I will also keep you from the hour of trial that is going to come on the whole world to test the inhabitants of the earth. I am coming soon. Hold on to what you have, so that no one will take your crown.*

"The one who is victorious I will make a pillar in the temple of my God. Never again will they leave it. I will write on them the name of my God and the name of the city of my God, the new Jerusalem, which is coming down out of heaven from my God; and I will also write on them my new name" (NIV).

Things to ponder:

Do you feel you have a message to share that would bring God glory?

Would you be willing to join God's army of women?

Have you prepared your soul with the armor of love?

Do you want to see other women walk in the Father's love?

Daily Devotions:

Now whose truth are you believing about yourself?

List two incidents where you have believed rightly about yourself:

1.

2.

Make Father God your mirror. *"You are the righteousness of God in Christ Jesus"* (script). *"My God shall supply all my needs according to His riches in glory"* (Script). You are God's magnum opus. Take time to think about how carefully He's designed you (Psalm 139:13-14) and how much He loves you (John 3:16).

Through these Scriptures, describe how you believe God sees you:

LESSON TWELVE

In Your Own Words

Who do you believe you are?
(Circle One)

Victory ◆ Glory ◆ Joy ◆ Fire

From the day you were born God has recorded every moment of your life. He loves you and He cares for you more than you could possibly understand!

My Prayer For You

Dearest Father, restore my beautiful sister and show her how much she means to You. Strengthen and encourage her, she needs You to love her into wholeness. Use all the pain and atrocities she's experienced to make her stronger and wiser. Let her experience Your immense favor and keep her always in Your heart. Release her and make her an effective witness for your kingdom

God bless YOU!

In Jesus' name!

In Your Own Words

This chapter is dedicated to you and the struggle, victory and passion of your life. In your own words, tell your story:

Other Books by Victoria Boyson

The Birth of Your Destiny: Just like a baby hidden in the womb, so are the promises God has given to us. He speaks to us of our future as if to conceive within us His will and purpose for our lives. Experience an impartation of God's grace and faith to fulfill all that God has for you through this powerful and insightful book.

His Passionate Pursuit: Victoria challenges you to embrace the captivating revelations of His passion for you - His beloved bride. It is an invitation to an awakening encounter with God. His Passionate Pursuit is a portal to heaven, unleashing God s presence into your life, empowering you with an impartation from His heart.

Awakening: The Deep Sleep (A Visionary Journey): With the fate of the world in the balance, Beloved must rise above the deceptive snares of her adversaries to fulfill her calling: to pursue the prophetic host and liberate the slumbering army of the Lord. Destined to wage war against the darkness, the army must be awakened to destroy the enemy's grasp on this world.

To contact the author or to order more copies of God's Magnum Opus, please visit her website at www.VictoriaBoyson.com.

God's Magnum Opus is also available through Amazon.com, Christian bookstores and other online bookstores. It is also available as an eBook, purchasable through Amazon.com.

You can follow Victoria Boyson on Facebook, Twitter and Goodreads.

Check out the many resources on her website and sign up for her enewsletter at: www.VictortiaBoyson.com.

ANSWER KEY

Lesson One:

Part 1 – woman; not good, very good; (powerful) helper, equal; lesser quality; together

Part 2 – companion, property; magnum opus; grand finale; perception; chaos; consequence Dream; Genesis 3:15 study (In your own words)

Part 3 – equal partners; no; half

Part 4 – Greek myth; who was with her; who was with her; share; y'all or (plural you)

Lesson Two:

Part 1 – God; man or Adam's rib, woman; need; God's; dependent; Jewish teachings; source

Part2 – lived; imitate or follow; among the Lord's people; no; to win people to Christ

Part 3 – You will strike his heel; fear; women; grace; women; grace; abuse towards women

Part 4 – greatest gifts; Adam; devalue; (In your own words); dishonors himself; equality

Lesson Three:

Part 1 – troublemakers; Levite, concubine; get up, it's time to get going or (Judges 19:28); twelve pieces, 400,000 men

Part 2 – 26,000 soldiers, 22,000 soldiers; 18,000 soldiers, Judges 20:28; 25,000 soldiers; 65,000 soldiers

Part 3 – experienced swordsmen; valuable, precious treasure; daughter; you, you; gave His own Son; (In your own words)

Part 4 – NOT; God; Bathsheba; love; go; Bathsheba

Lesson Four

Part 1 – the cross; Jesus; authority; vanishes; one in Christ; work on the cross; no longer

Part 2 – no; on earth as it is in heaven; equally; yes; conditions

Part 3 – bias; (In your own words); (In your own words); raise up; Galatians 3:28; as it is in heaven

Part 4 – greater works, kingdom; (In your own words); know Him; 1. Know the Gospel 2. Live the Gospel 3. Preach the Gospel

Lesson Five

Part 1 – 1. Women (In your own words) 2. Women (In your own words) 3. Women (In your own words); you; deliver; women; imprisoned; freedom; slavery; slavery

Part 2 – Mary Magdalene, Mary the mother of Jesus, Mary Salome, Martha, Miriamne, Susanna and Joanna are the women most commonly known as the female disciples, but only heaven's history knows if this list is complete; His Father; harvest

Part 3 – justice or vengeance; knelt, sand; humanity or worth; for man; People or Women

Part 4 – divorce; male and female, united, one flesh, God; send her away; hearts were hard, commits adultery; original design; His will, women

Lesson Six:

Part 1 – Greek mythology; Greek; souls; Roman, Jewish; woman

Part 2 – No; tongues, prophecy and women; ministry gifts; prophesy

Part 3 – revolutionary; Priscilla; co-workers or co-laborers; women in ministry; Romans 16:1-2; same or equal; outstanding among the apostles; Lydia and Chloe

Part 4 – Paul; husbands; teach; minister

Part 5 – slavery; Jewish nation; Israelis; thousands of years, owned; scare; NOT

Lesson Seven

Part 1 – way of love; love; Leviticus 19:18; apostles; new

Part 2 – disciples; theology; servant-hood; mutual; not; (In your own words)

Part 3 – hierarchy; love; equal; Christ; NOT, NOT, NOT; women, slaves or the poor; church

Part 4 – very careful; way of love; way of love; slaves; Christ, display or reveal; children; husbands; Christ; love

Part 5 – Submission; obedience; choice; voluntary yielding; voluntarily yielded; demanded or forced; humanity; submission; Humanity

Lesson Eight:

Part 1 – ministry; dishonor; patient; appreciates; envy; self; women; others; dominate; protects

Part 2 – (In your own words); (In your own words); (In your own words); degrade; men, women; GOD; art; love; humanity; (In your own words)

Part 3 – Luke 10:2; half; darkness

Part 4 – No; tongues, prophecy; disorderly; submissive; love; reiterating; love; believers; Greek; love; attitude; hearer; humble

Part 5 – no punctuations; rebuttal; left out; NO; restating

Lesson Nine:

Part 1 – Priscilla, debauchery; pagan beliefs, not; "Cling to your faith in Christ"; urge, pray; argue, debate

Part 2 – not likely; likewise, also; profess; promiscuity; professed; inclusive

Part 3 – women, woman; error, truth; submission; one; professor; teaching

Part 4 – homes; unlikely; woman in error; woman; Eve; insult, taught; deceived, teach; source, one

Part 5 – understood; Savior; childbearing; seed or offspring; deceived

Part 6 – standards; women; silence or stop

Lesson Ten:

Part 1 – obedience, Bible or Scriptures; Exodus 15:20; Judges 4:4; Judges 4:18; Joshua 2:1-16 or James 2:25; 2 Kings 22:14; Esther 1-8; Luke 2:36; Luke 8:1-3; Luke 10:38-42; John 4:27-38; Luke 1:42-45; Luke 1:47-55; Acts 9:36-42

Part 2 – underestimated; Israel; Deborah; home; Sisera; milk; tent; hammer, tent peg; temple; Jael; warrior

Part 3 – singing, preaching; William J. Seymour; harvest; women, marriage; ministry, women; reform; activism, reform; Word of God

Part 4 – Nun, wife; prayer; intimate; ecstasy; prophesy; heresy; persecution

Part 5 – harvested; lies; spirit realm; vital; entire; YOU

Lesson Eleven:

Part 1 – division; Genesis 1:27; Job 38:29; Isaiah 42:14; Isaiah 42:3-4; Isaiah 66:13; Spirit; superiority; argue; humble; small distinction; war on women; against

Part 2 – equal; traditional; no; good; human; qualified

Part 3 – understanding; important; relationship; role; choice; women; your

Part 4 – gauge or standard; women; bad; value

Part 5 – no; man; calling or ministry; pressure; represent; (In your own words)

Part 6 – struggle